Jimmie Goes to CHURCH

by Gladys Rhiner
pictures by Janet Smalley

THIRD PRINTING

Library of Congress Catalog No. 57-6327

© 1957

BROADMAN PRESS   Nashville, Tennessee

"When can I go to the preaching service, Mommie?" Jimmie asked one day.

Mommie smiled at Jimmie.

"Would you like to go next Sunday?" she asked.

"Oh, yes," said Jimmie.

"I'm going to church. I'm going to church," sang Jimmie when Daddy came home that night.

"Well, that's fine," said Daddy.
"When?"

"Next Sunday," said Jimmie climbing into Daddy's lap.

All week Jimmie ran to Mommie every morning and asked, "Is it Sunday today?"

"No, not today," Mommie said.

All week Mommie talked to Jimmie about going to church.

She told him how the sun came through the church windows.

She told him about the bright flowers in tall vases.

She told him about the big Bible on the pulpit stand.

She told him the preaching service was a special time to learn more about Jesus.

At last it was Sunday. When Jimmie was dressed, Daddy called him. He and Daddy opened Jimmie's money box.

Jimmie took some money for his church offering.

"Shall I keep it for you until after Sunday school?" asked Daddy.
"All right," said Jimmie.

Jimmie went with Mommie and Daddy to Sunday school.

Jimmie saw other people going to Sunday school too.

Jimmie could hear the church bells ringing.

"Come-to-church, come-to-church," they seemed to say.

Mommie came for Jimmie when
Sunday school was over.

"We must hurry in to church,"
she said. "Daddy is waiting for us."

Jimmie slipped his hand into hers
and skipped along.

Outside they met Daddy.

Daddy gave Jimmie his money for the offering, and Jimmie put the money in his pocket.

Then Daddy took Jimmie's hand
and they walked around the building
to the church door.

"We must go into the church
quietly," Mommie said as they
climbed the steps to the door.

At the door, an usher shook
hands with Jimmie and gave him a
church bulletin.

"We'll find a seat where Jimmie
can see the preacher," the usher said.

He led them down the aisle to
seats near the front.

Jimmie felt so grown up sitting
with Mommie and Daddy in church.

The organ was playing soft music.
Jimmie listened to the music. He
felt all still inside.

He knew the chorus of the hymn the people were singing. Jimmie loved to sing. So when they sang the chorus he stood very tall and sang too.

Oh, how I love Jesus,
Oh, how I love Jesus, . . .
Because He first loved me.

He listened quietly as the preacher read verses from the big Bible on the pulpit stand.

He watched the ushers as they passed the offering plates. When Daddy held the plate for him, Jimmie placed his money on the plate.

That made him feel good. It
made him feel important too.

Daddy had told him part of his
money would help buy new song
books for the church.

And part of his money would be sent across the ocean where many little boys and girls did not know about Jesus.

Part of his money would help a little boy or girl in a hospital somewhere to be well and strong again.

Daddy said that Jimmie's money could help do lots of good things for people.

Jimmie heard the preacher thank God for all the money the people had given. So he bowed his head too.

"Thank you, God, for everything," Jimmie whispered to God.

The choir began to sing. Jimmie liked to hear the choir sing. All the voices sounded a little like the music the organ played.

Jimmie hummed a little hum, very quietly to himself.

Jimmie listened carefully to the preacher. He didn't understand everything the preacher said. But he understood some things.

"Jesus loves everyone, boys and girls, men and women," the preacher said.

Jimmie understood that.

After the service was over, Jimmie stopped with Mommie and Daddy to speak to the preacher.

The preacher shook Jimmie's hand.

"Jimmie," he said, "I'm glad you came to church today. Come every Sunday. We need you here."

Jimmie smiled at the preacher. He felt all good inside. He was important.

"Yes, sir," he said to the preacher, as he took Daddy's hand again.